Small Steps

toward

Transforming Grief

a guided journal
by Peter Burke

—

one of a series of
Journals for Seekers™

Small Steps to Transforming Grief: A Guided Journal by Peter Burke, one of a series of Journals for Seekers™. Copyright 2019 Peter Burke. Cover design by Adrienne Fritze. Photo by pawel szvmanski on Unsplash. Interior design by Elisabeth McCumber.

This book belongs to

_____

May I feel and accept all my emotions and physical sensations, knowing that hiding from pain prolongs it.

May I come to grips with today's reality and patiently puzzle out a path to tomorrow.

May I take care of my body and spirit by eating, drinking, exercising, staying in touch with friends, praying for guidance, and taking both small and large steps toward a brighter future.

—Peter Burke

Introduction

You who meant so much to me can never be replaced. What am I going to do now that you are gone? Can what happened to you happen to me?

Are these thoughts on your mind?

My personal experiences with grief started when I was seven and lasted for the next twenty years. For decades after, I guarded myself against feeling grief, showing no response to any bad news – like this ...

> *When they tell me you are dead,*
> *my skull will shrink, my eyes will burn.*
> *I'll try to moan, but my throat will close.*
> *I'll not believe that you are gone*
> *while I still live.*
>
> *That's what I'll feel.*
> *Here's what I'll do.*
>
> *"Thank you," I'll say, "for telling me.*
> *Does this mean I'll have to move?*
> *Should I call Cousin Louise?"*
> *I'll continue setting the table*
> *for one less.*

I created this journal to help you work through numb-ness, despair, and disorganization by using your three basic human talents — feeling, thinking and acting; or if you like, your heart, your head and your hands. It provides pathways to accepting your emotions, dealing with your new reality, and caring for yourself. Creating it has been difficult, but it has helped me move out of the past and into the present. I hope it does the same for you.

> *Walk around feeling like a leaf.*
> *Know you could tumble any second.*
> *Then decide what to do with your time.*
>
> —*Naomi Shehab Nye*

You never "get over" grief. But you can transform how you relate to grievous events, past and present. You can develop the serenity to accept what you can't change, the courage to change what you can, and the wisdom to know the difference.

Suggestions for Using Your Heart (Feeling)

For feeling emotions, words work.

What would happen if you wrote, discussed, labeled, made lists — anything — to put names to what your heart is feeling?

> *Give sorrow words.*
> *The grief that does not speak*
> *Whispers the o'er fraught heart*
> *And bids it break.*
>
> —*Shakespeare*

For feeling physical sensations, focus works.

What would you discover if you focused on the physical feelings in every part of your body? Take at least five minutes, letting your body feel and react. Relax your eyes and jaw. Breathe in through your nose and out through your mouth as you do this. What hurts? What is tight? What does your body want?

> *Feeling is healing.*
>
> — *John F. Barnes, PT*

Suggestions for Using Your Head (Thinking)

What could you figure out if you first wrote a description of where you are now, then looked for paths forward?

What have you lost? What do you still have?

Who is there to help you?

What can you find to look forward to?

Suggestions for Using Your Hands (Acting)

What would happen if you asked for help? Prayed for guidance? Treated your body with slow stretches? or long walks? Took care of yourself by cooking dinner? or making bread? Helped out a friend? or a stranger? Listed your evening gratitudes and blessings?

Use this Journal at Your Own Pace

Use it once a day, once a week, or just now and then. Day 2 does not need to tread on the heels of Day 1. Be private and solitary, or find someone to check in with as you work your way through.

Your absence has gone through me
Like thread through a needle.
Everything I do is stitched with its color.

—W. S. Merwin

Day 1

*Write a few words to set the stage
for working through this journal.*

DAY ONE

Here is where I am today:

_____

_____

_____

_____

I am grieving because:

_____

_____

_____

_____

I am taking care of myself by:

_____

_____

_____

_____

_____

DAY ONE

What more do I need to do?

My ten-day goal is:

Day 2

Write a bit about your feelings, thoughts and actions.

DAY TWO: FEEL

Today, my words are:
(example – numb, angry)

___

___

___

___

___

Today, my body sensations are:
(example – chest pain)

___

___

___

___

___

DAY TWO: THINK

Today, I know that I have lost:
(example – my life partner)

___

___

___

___

... but I also know that I still have:
(example – my children)

___

___

___

___

... and can do:
(example – ask for advice)

___

___

___

___

DAY TWO: ACT

Today I will nurture myself
by taking these actions:
*(example – write an angry letter and throw it
away; lie still and focus on my heart as I breathe)*

Day 3

Continue the work.

DAY THREE: FEEL

Today, my words are:

_____

_____

_____

_____

Today, my body sensations are:

_____

_____

_____

_____

_____

_____

_____

_____

DAY THREE: THINK

Today, I know that I have lost:

_____
_____
_____
_____
_____

... but I also know that I still have:

_____
_____
_____
_____
_____

... and can do:

_____
_____
_____
_____
_____

DAY THREE: ACT

Today I will nurture myself
by taking these actions:

Day 4

Focus on words of emotion.

DAY FOUR: FEEL

Today, I use words to elaborate on my feelings of loss.

DAY FOUR: THINK

Today, I describe what I might be able to do to accept or change my emotions.

DAY FOUR: ACT

Today, I will take the following actions.

(Example: I will seek out a trusted companion and express my feelings.

Day 5

Focus on physical sensations.

DAY FIVE: FEEL

Today, my body feels:
I will be specific in describing my body sensations

DAY FIVE: THINK

What actions might help me cope with the tension or pain or numbness in my body?
(examples – lying on a roller or ball, stretching, taking a walk, doing it regularly.)

DAY FIVE: ACT

Today, I will nurture myself
by taking these actions:

Day 6

Focus on seeking help.

DAY SIX: FEEL

Today, this is how I feel about asking for help:

_____

_____

_____

_____

What kind of help do I feel that I need.

_____

_____

_____

_____

What can I research in the library or online to meet my current needs?

_____

_____

_____

_____

_____

Who do I know that can be of help? How?
(Be specific and realistic)

DAY SIX: ACT

Today, I will nurture myself
by taking these actions:

Day 7

Be visual.

DAY SEVEN: SKETCH

Today, I will draw sketches or cartoons about my grief:

DAY SEVEN: SKETCH

DAY SEVEN: SKETCH

Day 8

Write freely.

DAY EIGHT: FREE WRITE

Today, I will write poetry or scribble words about my grief.

DAY EIGHT: FREE WRITE

DAY EIGHT: FREE WRITE

Day 9

Focus on looking forward.

DAY NINE: FEEL

Today, I feel discouraged by these problems:

_____

_____

_____

_____

_____

_____

_____

and I feel encouraged by this good news:

_____

_____

_____

_____

_____

_____

_____

_____

DAY NINE: THINK

Today, I can reduce these problems by:

_____

_____

_____

_____

_____

_____

_____

Today, I can increase the good things by:

_____

_____

_____

_____

_____

_____

_____

DAY NINE: ACT

Today, I will nurture myself
by taking these actions:

Day 10

*After completing Day 10,
compare your entries to Days 2 and 3.*

DAY TEN: FEEL

Today, my words are:

_____

_____

_____

_____

_____

_____

Today, my body sensations are:

_____

_____

_____

_____

_____

_____

_____

DAY TEN: THINK

Today, I know that I have lost:

_____

_____

_____

_____

... but I also know that I still have:

_____

_____

_____

_____

... and can do:

_____

_____

_____

_____

DAY TEN: ACT

Today I will nurture myself by taking these actions:

Musings

MUSINGS

Looking back after ten days,
what new feelings am I sensing?

MUSINGS

What new thoughts are emerging?

MUSINGS

What helpful actions have I taken?

___

Looking forward to the next ten days, what will I work on next?

(examples – accepting my feelings and my body; setting my loss in the greater context of my life; acting to nourish myself and my community)

MUSINGS

How will I go about it?

_____

_____

_____

_____

_____

_____

_____

Who will I tell? and work with?

_____

_____

_____

_____

_____

_____

_____

Resources

In 2016, Holly Barker founded *Grief Anonymous* (grief anonymous.com), a place where grievers can communicate with one another (free) and find access to other grief support resources, such as Grief Resource Network (grief resourcenetwork.com).

Tara Brach (tarabrach.com) and Lizzy Hill (breathandbodywellness.com) are remarkably calm teachers of self-acceptance and meditation, using both rational thinking and felt understanding. I particularly like these two free meditations. (https://www.tarabrach.com/brief-meditation-5-minute/) and (http://www.breathandbodywellness.com/yoga-nidra/)

John W. James and Russell Friedman wrote *The Grief Recovery Handbook* to guide one through steps to say goodbye to a loss, including writing a goodbye letter. (griefrecoverymethod.com).

About Peter Burke

Grief came early to me. I was seven when my father had a severe stroke. I was fourteen when my mother developed leukemia. They both passed when I was twenty-six. I spent those years in suspended animation, expecting them to die at any moment. For decades after, I guarded myself against feeling grief, showing no response to any bad news. Even so, my life went on—college, work, marriage, family, divorce, remarriage. I passed as productive but was using half my energy to protect myself against fear and grief. Now, by writing Journals for Seekers, I intend to use my experience to help others develop a variety of life skills, including grieving. More than ever, I realize that shutting down pain also shuts down the possibility of joy.

www.ingramcontent.com/pod-product-compliance
Lightning Source LLC
Chambersburg PA
CBHW070844110526
R18273300001B/R182733PG44587CBX00001B/1